PUZZLE MASTERS
STAR QUEST

Cosmic colour codes by Lauren Farnsworth
and John Woodcock
Extreme mazes by Dr Gareth Moore
Star to stars by Sarah Wade
Illustrated by Chelen Écija

Written by Jonny Leighton
Consultancy by Stuart Atkinson
Edited by Jonny Leighton and Imogen Williams
Designed by Zoe Bradley and Jack Clucas
Cover designed by Angie Allison

Buster Books

INTRODUCTION

Welcome Puzzle Master. Are you ready for the ultimate puzzle challenge and a journey through the stars?

This book is packed with epic colouring puzzles, tricky galactic mazes, out-of-this-world join-the-dot challenges, and amazing cosmic facts about space travel and the universe.

Read the puzzle instructions opposite before you begin, then put your puzzle skills to the test with these fiendish challenges. Why not time yourself and fill in how long each puzzle takes you to complete in the space provided?

If you get a bit stuck, you can find all the answers at the back of the book.

COSMIC COLOUR CODES

Each puzzle is a numbered pattern. Colour in the spaces by following the colour code that appears beside the puzzle. If there isn't a number in a space, leave it blank. Gradually, a hidden picture will emerge.

Don't worry if you don't have pens and pencils in exactly the same shade as the colours shown. Get creative and make darker shades by pressing harder, or blend colours together if you need to.

EXTREME MAZES

Find your way through the Asteroid Belt, Saturn's rings and more in the extreme-maze challenges. Avoid taking wrong turns; you don't want to get lost in space!

STAR TO STARS

Connect the numbered stars to reveal a cosmic image.

Begin with number 1, which is marked with a large, hollow star. Connect the stars in number order until you reach the next hollow star. Then, take your pen off the page and look for the next number, which will also have a hollow star. Continue connecting the stars in the correct order until you reach the final large, hollow star.

You can use coloured pencils to complete each puzzle. Once you have joined all the stars, try colouring in the finished picture.

AWESOME ASTRONAUTS

The word 'astronaut' comes from Greek, and means 'star sailor'.

Astronauts wear spacesuits, which help them breathe in the vacuum of space and protect them from space debris.

In Russia, astronauts are called 'cosmonauts'. In China, they're called 'taikonauts'.

Over 500 women and men have been into space and more are being trained all the time.

1
2
3
4
5
6
7
8
9
10
11
12

TIME: ....

SHUTTLE LAUNCH PAD

When the Space Shuttle was in service, over 170 technicians and engineers worked on the launch pad, preparing the rocket for take off.

It took around a month to prepare the launch pad for a Space Shuttle launch.

Astronauts made final preparations in the 'White Room' and would walk through the 'orbiter access arm' to get to the shuttle's side hatch.

During the rocket's acceleration, the main engines would burn half a million gallons of fuel, made up of liquid hydrogen and liquid oxygen.

TIME: ....

SPUTNIK 1

Sputnik 1 was the first ever human-made object in space. It launched on 4th October, 1957.

It orbited the Earth 1,440 times in total, once every 96.2 minutes – not much longer than a football match.

It launched from the Baikonur Cosmodrome in the former Soviet Union and gave Russia the lead in the 'Space Race'.

Sputnik means 'fellow traveller' or 'companion' in Russian. Sputnik 2 carried a dog called Laika into space. She became the first animal to orbit the Earth.

TIME: ....

PLANET EARTH

1
2
3
4
5
6
7
8
9
10
11
12

Earth is the third planet from the Sun, the biggest rocky planet and the fifth largest planet in our Solar System.

The distance from Earth to the Sun is about 150 million kilometres.

Earth is home to towering volcanoes, soaring mountains, deep valleys and vast oceans. It is sometimes called the 'Blue Planet' because water covers approximately 71 percent of its surface.

Earth is made of four main layers: the inner core, the outer core, the mantle and the crust.

TIME: ....

ANDROMEDA GALAXY

Andromeda is a spiral galaxy like our own Milky Way, and is believed to contain over one trillion stars.

Andromeda is over two million light years away, and the closest major galaxy to the Milky Way. A light year is the distance light travels in one year, which is roughly 9.5 trillion kilometres.

Andromeda and the Milky Way are moving towards each other at over 100 kilometres per second. However, they are not expected to collide for over four billion years.

On a clear night you can actually see the Andromeda Galaxy with the naked eye; it looks like a tiny smudge.

TIME: ....

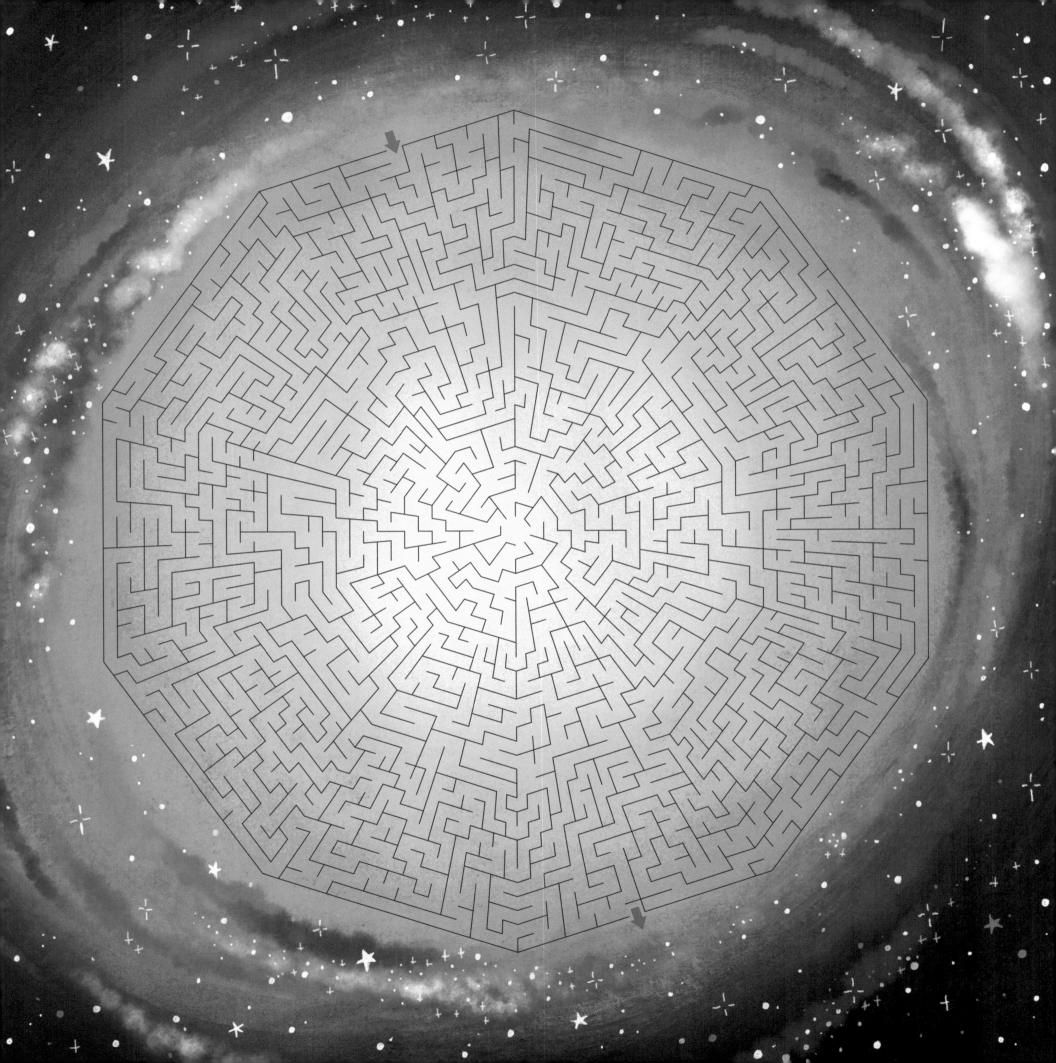

CURIOSITY ROVER

The Curiosity rover is a large, mobile laboratory, designed for use on Mars, the fourth closest planet to the Sun.

The rover is 3 metres long, has 6-wheel drive and on-board cameras to help the mission team back on Earth decide where to explore.

The rover discovered that Mars used to have an environment that may have supported microbial life.

The rover successfully landed in Gale Crater in August 2012, after a 9-month-long journey through space.

TIME: ....

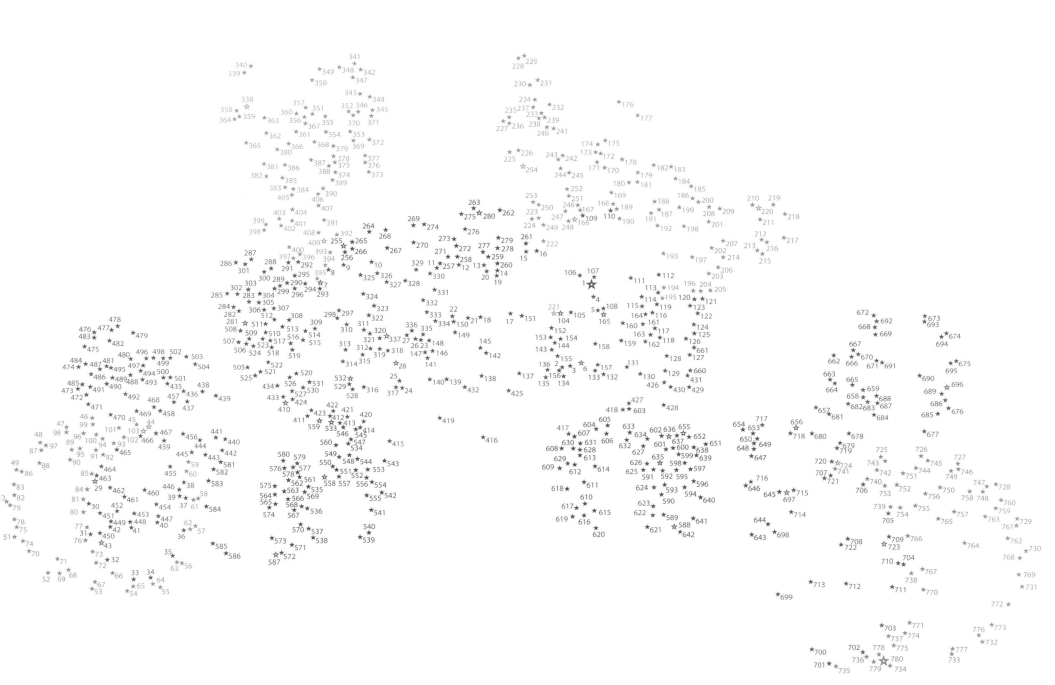

CAT'S EYE NEBULA

Most planetary nebulae, like the Cat's Eye Nebula, form when red giant stars begin falling apart at the end of their lives.

The vast amounts of gas ejected from these red giant stars form a colourful shell around the hot core. The word 'nebula' describes them perfectly, as it comes from the Latin for 'cloud'.

This particularly beautiful nebula is a staggering 3,362 light years away from Earth.

The Cat's Eye Nebula is made up of at least 11 concentric circles of gas that surround the inner core of the dying star.

1
2
3
4
5
6
7
8
9
10
11
12
13
14
15
16

TIME: ....

SPACE WALK

Anytime an astronaut has to get out of a vehicle in space, they are doing something called a space walk.

The outside of the International Space Station (ISS) needs a lot of maintenance. The only way to do that is for astronauts to venture out themselves.

During a space walk, astronauts are connected to the space station by strong safety tethers. They also tether their tools to their spacesuits to stop them floating away.

The longest space walk in history was performed by Susan Helms and Jim Voss, lasting a staggering 8 hours and 56 minutes.

TIME: ....

HUBBLE SPACE TELESCOPE

The Hubble Space Telescope was launched into Earth's orbit in 1990. It takes photographs of stars, planets and galaxies.

It is named after Edwin Powell Hubble, a famous American astronomer, who discovered that there are galaxies beyond our own Milky Way.

The telescope has helped astronomers discover the age of the universe; it is now estimated to be a staggering 13.8 billion years old.

When it was launched, the telescope's images were blurry, so it had to be fitted with special 'glasses' to correct the lens.

TIME: ....

VOSTOK 1

Vostok 1 was the first spacecraft to carry a human into space.

It was launched by the Soviet Union on 12th April, 1961, carrying a 27-year-old pilot, Yuri Gagarin.

The rocket was not capable of landing so, at seven kilometres from the Earth's surface, Yuri Gagarin was ejected from the craft and parachuted to safety.

It took Yuri Gagarin 108 minutes to orbit the Earth in Vostok 1.

TIME: ....

THE SUN

The Sun, Earth's local star, is a giant ball of superheated gas at the heart of the Solar System.

Just like Earth, the Sun spins. It takes about 27 Earth days for the Sun to spin once on its axis.

The Sun is so vast that it accounts for 99 percent of all matter in our Solar System.

It takes eight minutes for sunlight from the Sun to reach the Earth.

TIME: ....

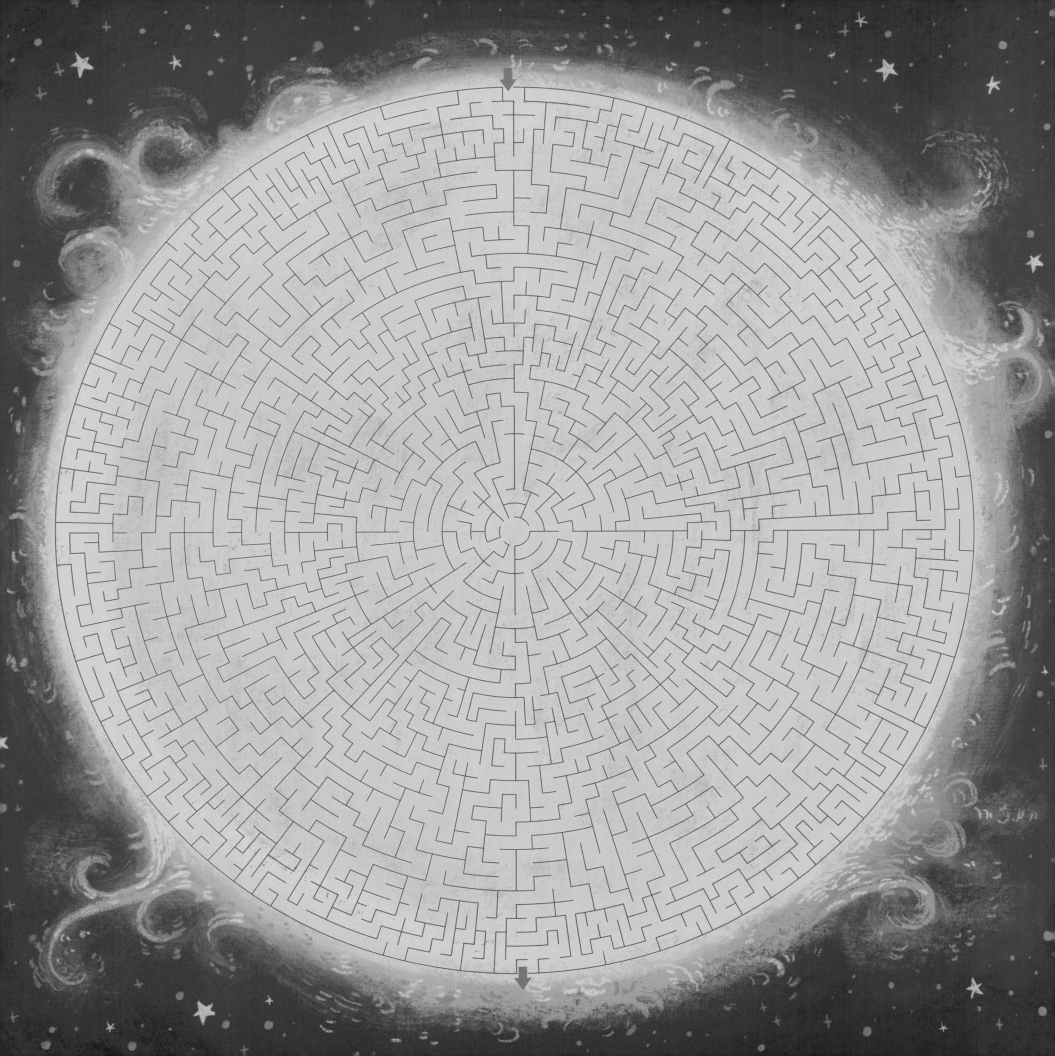

INTERNATIONAL SPACE STATION

The first piece of the International Space Station (ISS) was launched by Russia in 1998.

The ISS is a working laboratory, with science experiments being conducted by Russia, Japan, the US and Europe.

The ISS orbits the Earth 16 times a day. The lucky astronauts aboard get to see 16 sunrises and sunsets in 24 hours.

During their time off, astronauts on the ISS take photographs out of the windows or watch science fiction films on a big screen.

TIME: ....

EARTH RISE

The astronauts who went to the Moon got to see Earth 'rising' over the lunar horizon, just like the Sun 'rises' over the Earth.

Astronauts Frank Borman, Jim Lovell and William Anders were the first men to orbit the Moon on 24th December, 1968.

The Moon is thought to have been created when another planet the size of Mars crashed into the Earth around 4.5 billion years ago.

The gravity of the Moon affects life on Earth, regulating the tides from 384,000 kilometres away.

1
2
3
4
5
6
7
8
9
10
11
12
13
14

TIME: ....

ASTEROID BELT

The Asteroid Belt is estimated to contain between 1.1 and 1.9 million asteroids, and sits between the orbits of Mars and Jupiter.

Asteroids are made of rock, metal or mixtures of the two. They are the remnants of the early days of the Solar System, when the planets were being formed.

In the early days of the Solar System, the rocky planets were bombarded by asteroids. Now, large impacts are rare. However, the Earth is still hit by thousands of tiny meteorites every day.

In 1998, NASA created the Near-Earth Object Observations programme to detect any asteroid potentially hazardous to life on Earth.

TIME: ....

CANIS MAJOR

This constellation – a group of stars that appear to form a pattern in the sky – contains Sirius, the 'dog star', which is the brightest star in Earth's night sky.

Canis Major represents the fastest canine in Greek mythology, 'Laelaps'. This legendary dog was said to catch anything it pursued.

The stars come together to represent a hunting dog, which follows its master, Orion, across the sky.

The constellation includes Adhara, a double star that is 430 light years away from Earth.

TIME: ....

MOON LANDING

1
2
3
4
5
6
7
8
9
10
11

Apollo 11 launched from Cape Kennedy, USA, on 16th July, 1969, carrying Neil Armstrong, Buzz Aldrin and Michael Collins.

On 20th July, 1969, the lunar lander, called the *Eagle*, glided gently on to the Moon's surface.

Armstrong was the first man out of the lander, and uttered the famous line: "One small step for man; one giant leap for mankind."

In total, 12 people have walked on the Moon, the most recent being astronaut Harrison Schmidt in 1972.

TIME: ....

LIFE ON THE ISS

The International Space Station (ISS) can be home to up to six astronauts at a time.

As well as important space experiments, astronauts have to keep themselves fit to avoid their muscles wasting away. They exercise for up to two hours a day.

Food comes mostly in packets, heated in the space oven on board. Salt and pepper come in liquid form, so that the tiny particles don't float away.

Astronauts have to strap themselves to their beds at night. They wouldn't want to bump into each other while they're dreaming.

TIME: ....

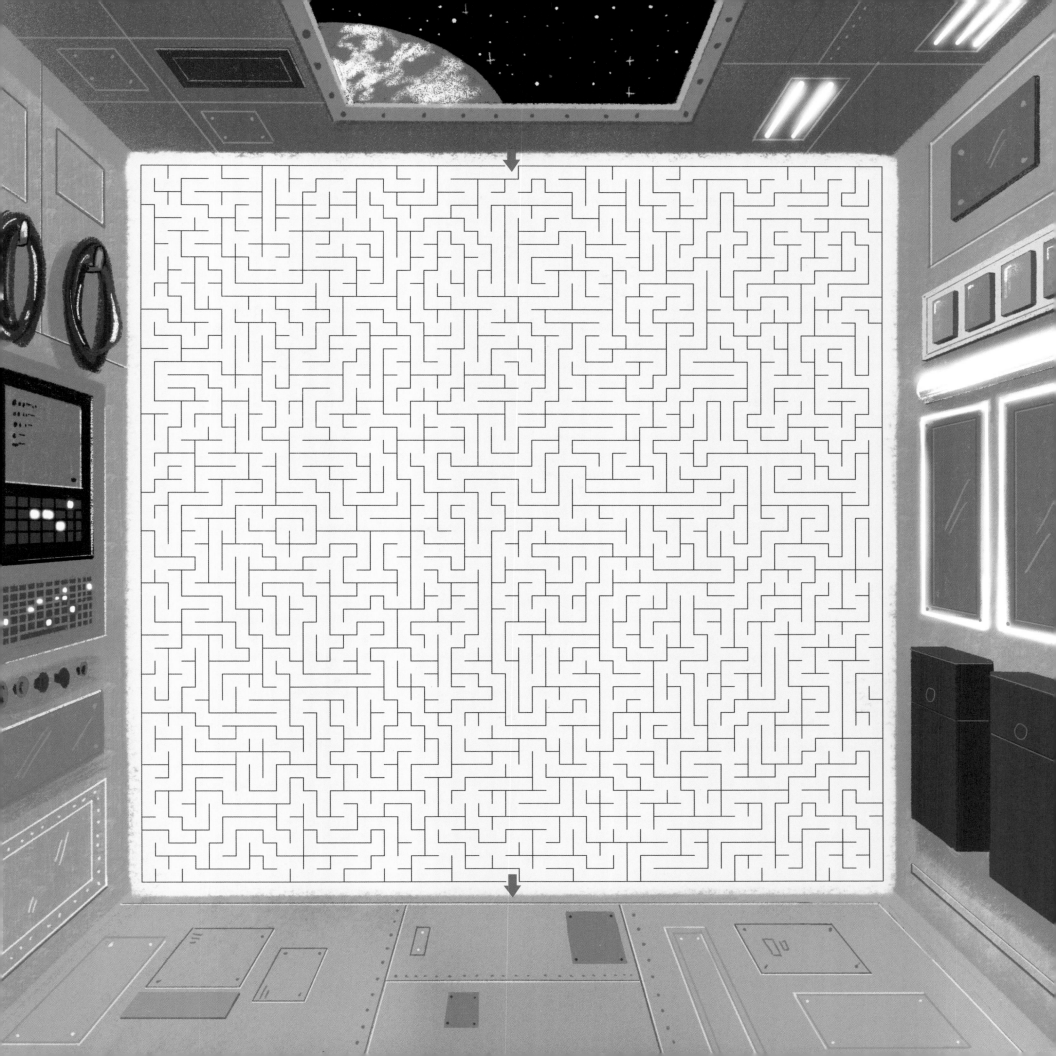

VOYAGER 1

Voyager 1 is one of two almost identical spacecraft that have gone further into the cosmos than any other human-made objects.

Together, Voyager 1 and 2 have visited all four of the major outer planets: Jupiter, Saturn, Uranus and Neptune, as well as many moons.

The Voyagers carry messages engraved on to golden records that contain music, images and sounds showing life and culture on Earth.

In August 2012, Voyager 1 made history when it left the Solar System and entered 'interstellar' space – this is the region of space between star systems.

TIME: ....

COSMIC COMETS

Comets are lumps of ice or rock that orbit the Sun just like planets. Some have short orbits measured in hundreds of days, others take hundreds of years.

When some of these rocky visitors approach the Sun they heat up, causing gas and ice to melt and form a 'tail' that trails behind the inner core.

Comets were formed in the early years of the Solar System, some 4.5 billion years ago.

Comets mostly come from two areas of deep space: the mysterious Oort Cloud and the distant Kuiper Belt.

1
2
3
4
5
6
7
8
9
10
11
12
13
14
15

TIME: ....

JUPITER

Jupiter is so big that if Earth were the size of a grape, Jupiter would be the size of a basketball.

Jupiter is twice as massive as all the other planets in our Solar System combined, and is over 8 million kilometres from the Sun.

Europa, one of Jupiter's moons, has the potential to host life. There is evidence of a water ocean below its crust.

In 1610, Galileo Galilei, an Italian astronomer and scientist, discovered Jupiter's four largest moons: Io, Europa, Ganymede and Callisto.

TIME: ....

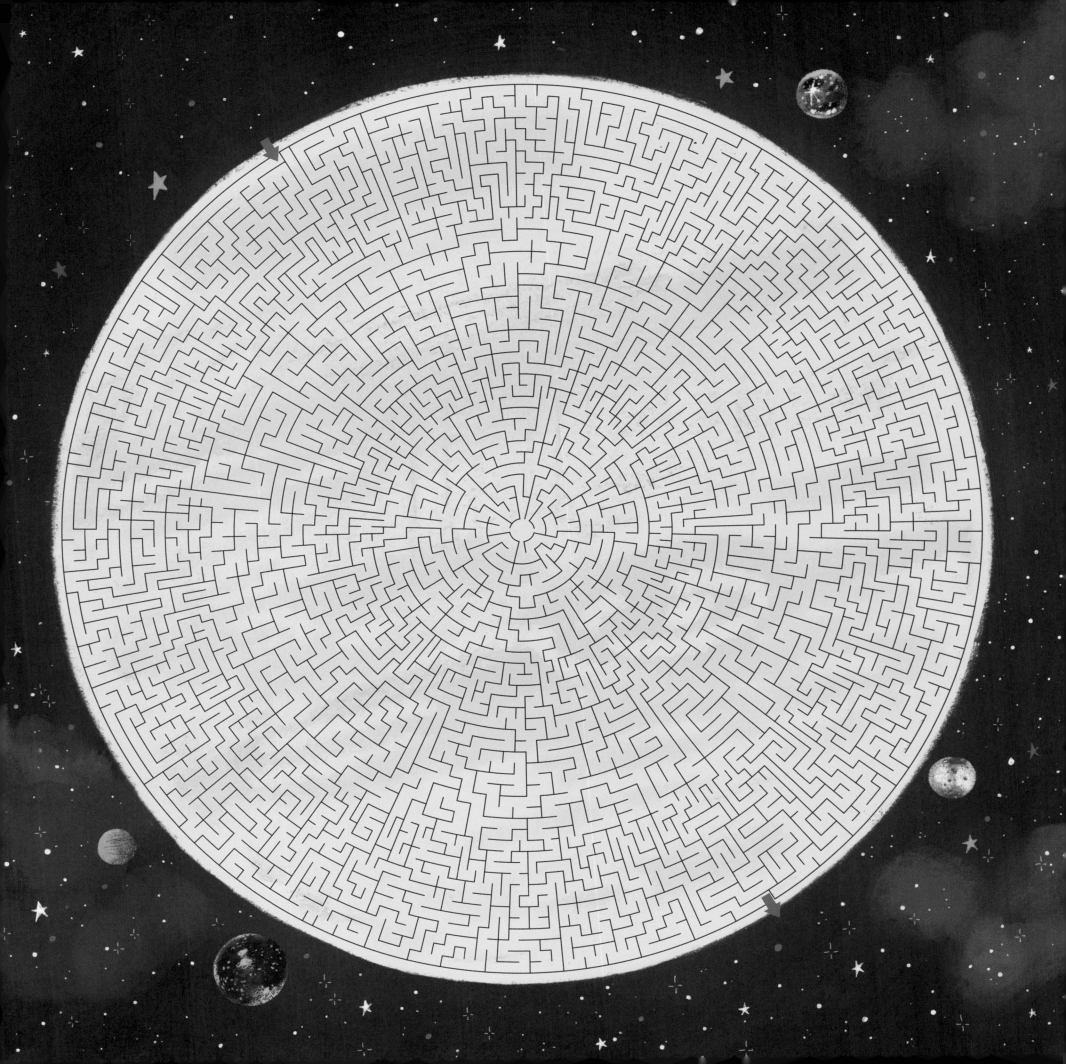

SPACE SHUTTLE

The first shuttle launched on 12th April, 1981. Between 1981 and 2011 the fleet flew 135 missions, and helped to build the International Space Station.

There were five amazing space ships in service over the years: *Columbia, Challenger, Discovery, Endeavour* and *Atlantis*.

Each ship's top speed was a cool 28,000 kilometres per hour.

The fleet travelled a mind-boggling 872,906,379 kilometres and orbited the Earth 21,152 times.

TIME: ....

FELIX BAUMGARTNER

This Austrian daredevil jumped out of a balloon almost 40 kilometres above New Mexico, USA, on 14th October, 2012.

It took 9 minutes 3 seconds for him to fall from the edge of space to the ground.

This skydiver was the first man to break the 'sound barrier' during freefall, travelling at an incredible 1,340 kilometres per hour.

At the edge of space, the air pressure is less than 2 percent of that at sea level.

1
2
3
4
5
6
7
8
9
10

TIME: ....

SATURN

Saturn is mostly made of gas. In theory, if there was a bath big enough, the planet would float in the water.

Winds in Saturn's atmosphere can reach up to 1,799 kilometres per hour.

In 2014, NASA spacecraft Cassini discovered what is believed to be a lake of liquid water under the frozen surface of Saturn's moon, Enceladus.

Saturn spins so quickly it is squashed at its poles. The planet is actually more oval shaped than round.

TIME: . . . .

GIGANTIC JUPITER

This is the largest planet in the Solar System and was named after the king of ancient Roman gods.

The planet is made up almost entirely of hydrogen and helium and takes just 10 hours to spin once on its axis.

Jupiter is home to the Great Red Spot, the biggest storm in the Solar System. The storm has been raging for hundreds of years and is wider than planet Earth.

Jupiter is the fifth planet from the Sun and astronomers believe it has at least 69 moons.

1
2
3
4
5
6
7
8
9
10
11
12
13
14

TIME: ....

SOLAR SYSTEM

The Solar System is home to Earth and the other seven major planets, as well as dwarf planets, moons, asteroids and comets.

It also extends far into space, encompassing the Kuiper Belt and the Oort Cloud, large and mysterious areas full of icy and rocky bodies.

Astronomers have discovered other solar systems around stars far away in space.

Our Solar System formed 4.5 billion years ago from a collapsing cloud of gas and dust.

TIME: ....

THE RINGED PLANET

Saturn is the sixth closest planet to the Sun. It is around 1.4 billion kilometres from our parent star.

Its rings are made mostly from rock and ice, shattered remnants of moons, comets and asteroids that were ripped apart by the planet's gravity.

Saturn spins much faster than Earth, making a day only 10 hours and 40 minutes long. One year on the planet is equivalent to 29 Earth years.

Spaceships can't land on Saturn as the surface is made up of gases and liquids.

TIME: ....

SATELLITES

These spacecraft are fundamental to the modern world. They can send and receive signals from anywhere on the Earth's surface.

Satellites are used for tracking weather patterns, telephone, TV and Internet communications, radio broadcasting and more.

There are over 1,700 satellites whizzing around the Earth, sending messages back and forth.

Satellites can be found as near as 160 kilometres to Earth, to 36,000 kilometres away.

1
2
3
4
5
6
7
8
9
10

TIME: ....

APOLLO 11 COMMAND MODULE

This capsule is part of Apollo 11, which launched on 16th July, 1969, carrying Neil Armstrong, Buzz Aldrin and Michael Collins to the Moon.

When the crew landed on the Moon, a camera attached to the lunar lander broadcast the moment live to an estimated half a billion people watching on TV.

On 24th July, the crew began their descent back to Earth. As they came through the planet's atmosphere, the temperature of the vehicle rose to 2,760 degrees Celcius.

Three giant parachutes were deployed to slow the command module down before it splashed into the Pacific Ocean.

TIME: ....

ALL THE ANSWERS

1 AWESOME ASTRONAUTS

4 PLANET EARTH

2 SHUTTLE LAUNCH PAD

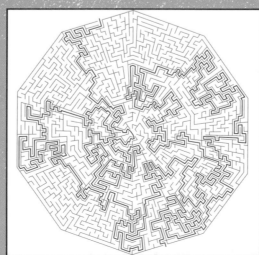

5 ANDROMEDA GALAXY

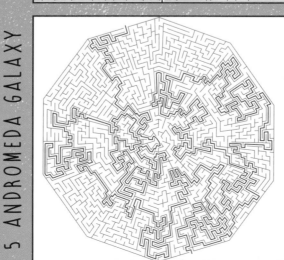

3 SPUTNIK I

6 CURIOSITY ROVER

7 CAT'S EYE NEBULA

8 SPACE WALK

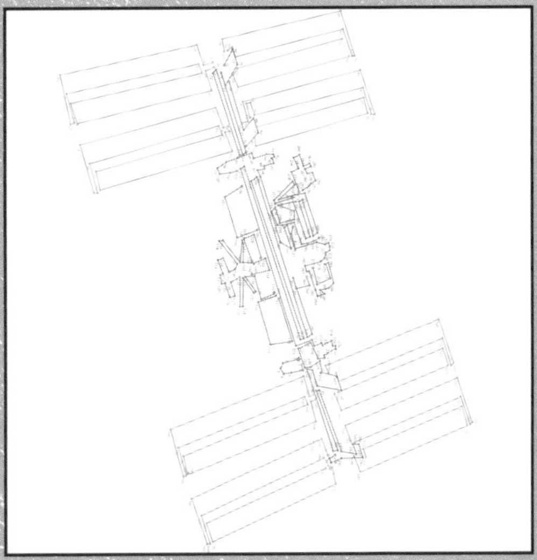

9 HUBBLE SPACE TELESCOPE

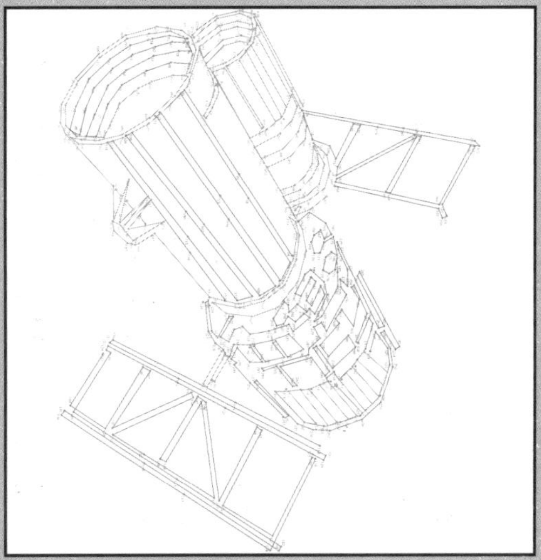

10 VOSTOK 1

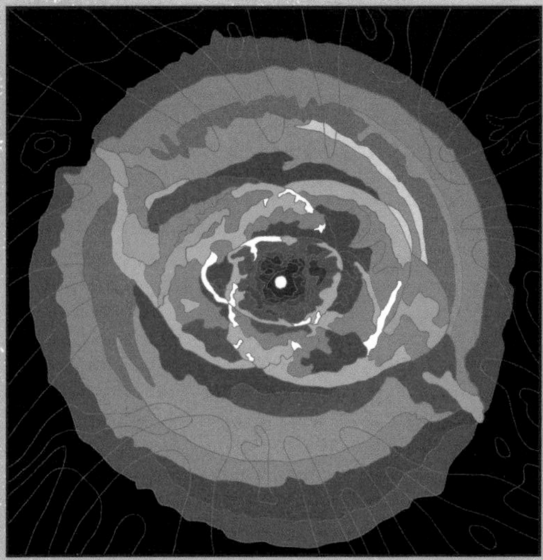

11 THE SUN

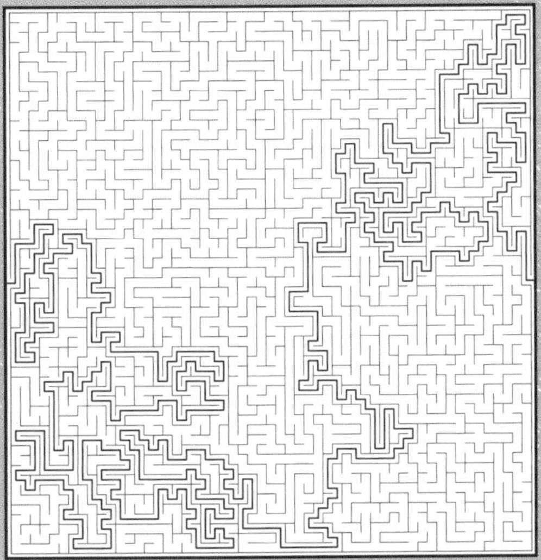

12 INTERNATIONAL SPACE STATION

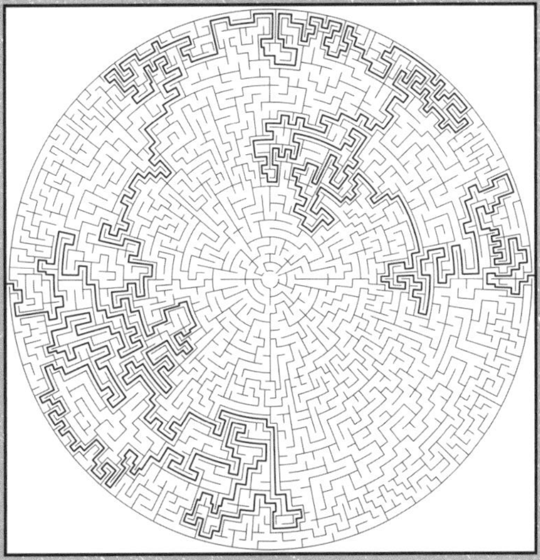

13 EARTH RISE

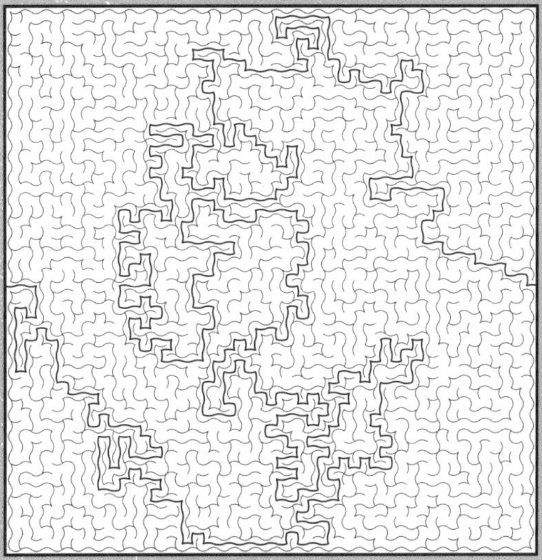

14 ASTEROID BELT

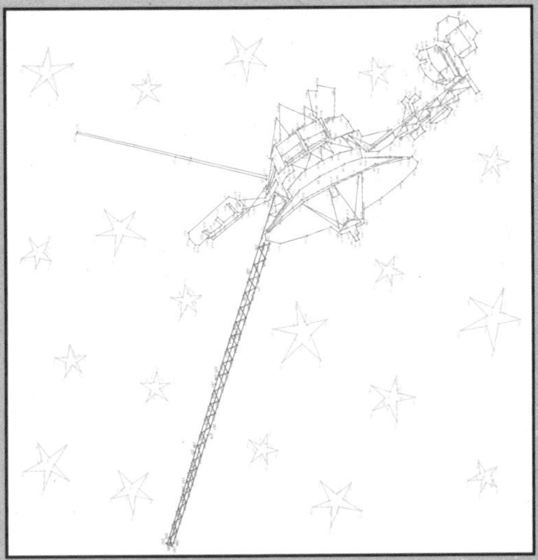

15 CANIS MAJOR

16 MOON LANDING

17 LIFE ON THE ISS

18 VOYAGER 1

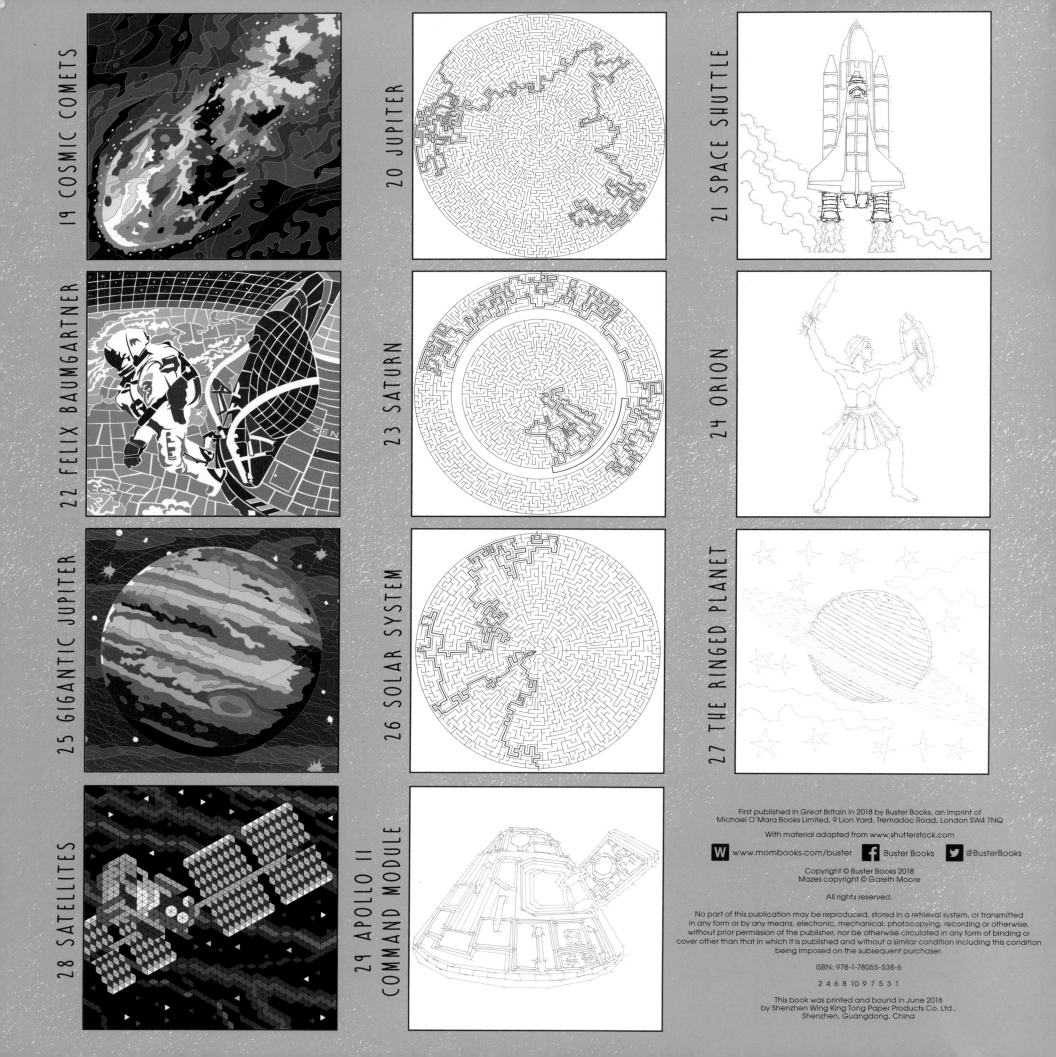

19 COSMIC COMETS

20 JUPITER

21 SPACE SHUTTLE

22 FELIX BAUMGARTNER

23 SATURN

24 ORION

25 GIGANTIC JUPITER

26 SOLAR SYSTEM

27 THE RINGED PLANET

28 SATELLITES

29 APOLLO 11 COMMAND MODULE

First published in Great Britain in 2018 by Buster Books, an imprint of
Michael O'Mara Books Limited, 9 Lion Yard, Tremadoc Road, London SW4 7NQ

With material adapted from www.shutterstock.com

W www.mombooks.com/buster F Buster Books T @BusterBooks

Copyright © Buster Books 2018
Mazes copyright © Gareth Moore

ISBN: 978-1-78055-538-6

2 4 6 8 10 9 7 5 3 1

This book was printed and bound in June 2018
by Shenzhen Wing King Tong Paper Products Co. Ltd.,
Shenzhen, Guangdong, China